Other books* by Malcolm Wells:

Solaria · with Harry Thomason and Bob Homan

Energy Essays

How to Buy Solar Heating without Getting Burnt · with Irwin Spetgang

Underground Designs

Notes from the Energy Underground

Underground Plans Book I · with Sam Wells

Gentle Architecture

Sandtiquity · with Kappy Wells

Passive Solar Energy · with Bruce Anderson

The Children's Book of Solar Energy · with Tilly Spetgang

Classic Architectural Birdhouses and Feeders

Underground Buildings

How to Build An Underground House

The Successful Contractor

Designing Your Natural House · with Charles G. Woods

Perspective

* A folder describing those still in print is available from the author

INFRA STRUCTURES

By Malcolm Wells

Photographs by Rick Friedman

2.

Printed in Singapore by Tien Wah Press. Mechanical production by K Design Studio, Brewster, Massachusetts.
Published in the United States of America 1994.

Library of Congress Catalog Card Number: 93-094043
Wells, Malcolm
INFRA STRUCTURES

Summary: Photographs and descriptions of America's crumbling and destructive infrastructure – roads, bridges, airports, etc. – contrasted with proposals for new, long-lasting public structures that will do far less harm to the land.

I.S.B.N. 0-9621878-6-0

Published by the author at the Underground Art Gallery
673 Satucket Road, Brewster, Cape Cod, Massachusetts 02631
(508) 896 6850   Fax: (508) 896 5116

* Rick Friedman's office is at 133 Beaconfield Road, Brookline, Massachusetts 02146.

I wish this book was worthy of being dedicated to all the non-human creatures of the world but since it's not, I'll have to settle for the wish alone.

Malcolm Wells

4.

"Infrastructure" doesn't appear in my trusty old 1949 Random House dictionary. There weren't as many ugly words back then. But the dictionary does, of course, have an entry for the prefix "infra-" meaning below or beneath. So infrastructure is the structure below, and you know what that means in terms of public awareness: out of sight, out of mind. Politically, it has meant let's not spend tax dollars on work no one will see.

It's not till a bridge falls into a river that we even think about what's holding it all up. And now, suddenly, we hear that not five or ten or a hundred bridges are unsafe; the number is in the hundreds of thousands!*

Add to that all the rusting tankfuls of radioactive wastes, the rotting piers and docks of our great seaports, and the rickety railroads, and you see an immense problem rising into the American consciousness. Every public structure in the country seems to have something wrong with it.

We can no longer hide from the problem. It's on the table now, and suddenly it's hot. Every other news show, it seems, now features either a pothole or a politician condemning potholes and waving the infra word in the air. Infrastructure is here to stay in spite of our short attention spans, and the work it suggests promises to be perhaps the greatest project of the next 50 years.

The other big jobs, reversing the environmental crisis and ending the divisiveness and violence that terrorize modern society, are in many ways linked to the decisions we'll make with regard to America's infrastructure. Are we up to the job? Will we use the same old failed ways or reach for a dream? Highways and railroads, airports and docks, housing and waterworks, just as much as our children, are our responsibility, for better or for worse. We can't pass the buck.

*34% of the nation's 600,750 bridges are substandard. – *Better Roads* magazine.

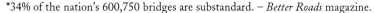

What a long way we've come from those hopeful days of mid-century and earlier! Back in the thirties, before his menace was recognized here, Hitler's superhighway, the Autobahn, captured the imagination of the world.

When New Jersey's highway department, influenced by the German designs, built its first cloverleaf intersection at Mays Landing in 1934, it was the talk of the state. Think how daring and improbable the design must have seemed to people still driving Model A Fords.

In 1939, the General Motors exhibit, Futurama, at the New York World's Fair took us through a wonderland, a dream world, in which teardrop-shaped cars soared along ribbons of concrete high above the farms and forests.

In the fifties, we saw Futurama's predictions confirmed in the graceful bridges of a Swiss engineer named Maillart, and by some of the more elegant stretches of the new interstate highway system then being constructed. Modern design, we felt, would before long solve all modern problems. Ignored at the time were the words of General Omar Bradley: "If we are not careful we shall leave our children a legacy of billion-dollar highways leading to places just like those they left behind." Did he actually foresee our look-alike strip malls and fast-food joints?

6.

But no one else seemed concerned. The boom was on, and for 40 years the surface of things seemed to be getting better in spite of the wars and the racial divisions that tore at our lives. Things, to most of us, looked pretty good if you didn't look too closely.

And then, one by one, they started to fall apart. A railroad bridge collapsed in New Jersey. Then a bridge in Ohio. Then a freeway in Connecticut. And along with those grim stories were the ever-growing numbers of potholes, decrepit railroad stations, rusting beams, and crumbling concrete. Suddenly they were all around us, everywhere.

So now here we are, faced with the need to go far beyond paint-up and patch-up before it's too late, before the public face of the United States resembles that of a Third World nation.

We don't have the money, but we will find it. The central issue is not the financial one. It is the *moral* one. That's what this book is all about. We know how to rebuild America's infrastructure, how to accommodate our almost mindless growth. We know how to do all the jobs involved. We have the work force needed to do them. We have the materials. And, as I said, we'll find the money. The only question remaining is whether we will replace our infrastructure with the same short-lived, land-destroying, boring, and often ugly structures or with long-lived, land-restoring, benign, exciting, and beautiful ones.

The way things look is sometimes an indication of society's values. You can see them at a glance in the way a society cares for itself. The all-too-visible decay of our cities expresses the racism, the superficiality, and the loss of pride that characterize us today. The poisoning and erosion of the continent's vast farmland, and the paving over of so much of it with houses and shopping centers, express our contempt for the living earth. The deterioration of America's infrastructure expresses our don't-bother-me-now attitude. If we retain that attitude when we rebuild, you can imagine the results.

Part of the problem may lie in the fact that we haven't yet imagined a better future. Simply replacing unsafe bridges – as necessary as it is – or rebuilding the railroads – would be pouring good money after bad. Do we want to be in the same mess again 30 or 40 years from now

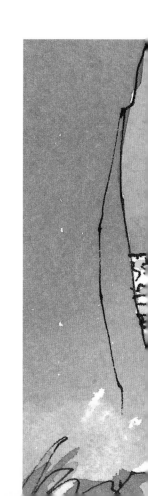

when all the replacements start to fail? Or is there a whole new way to live on this planet? Are human beings and the natural world destined to be at odds forever? Or can we, so long estranged from the world that produced us, learn to live as gently, as gracefully, and – with great good luck – as beautifully here as do all the rest of the world's creatures?

As you must surely suspect by now, this is not a book of engineering. I leave to the engineers the jobs they are so well equipped to handle. This is a book of possibilites, of "why not?," and of dreams. If we want our grandchildren – and *their* grandchildren – to walk upon a flowering earth, then the dreams will come true.

"If you have built castles in the air," wrote Henry Thoreau, "your work need not be lost; that is where they should be. Now put the foundations under them."

Malcolm Wells

My castles in the air have been castles in the earth ever since the moment in 1964 when, as the designer of a big pavilion at the New York World's Fair, I saw what I'd been doing to so much of the American land in my then 10 years as an up-and-coming architect. The revelation was not pleasant. Devastating would be more like it. Devastating revelation, devastating architecture.

I can't imagine why it took me so long to see that the most basic characteristic of all man-made constructions – that the primal essence of everything from a house to a parking lot – is its role as killer of living land. Only after that come such considerations as safety, cost, energy efficiency, style and so on. If a highway is safe or beautiful but still a land destroyer, it belongs on the minus side of the ledger. If a great new shipping pier is efficient and profitable but still a killer, what have we accomplished?

We've been so conditioned to see the construction around us as normal and acceptable it's almost impossible to think of buildings and roads, piers and airports, as having any lethal qualities at all. But lethal they are, and lethal they'll remain until we begin to see our uses of concrete and steel in that light. Otherwise, all the environmental arguments in the world will

leave the construction industry unmoved. This new, nature-based approach to design must not be limited to architecture and engineering – it's got to become the governing point of view for financiers, planners, developers, and politicians as well, and that means, in effect, everyone.

It took the gaudy, throwaway architecture of the World's Fair to open my eyes. My hope is that this book will open others'. As soon as I saw, on that summer day in New York, what I'd been doing to the forests and farms of the area I began to imagine another world, a world made green again not *in spite of* the built environment, but *because* of it. Earth covered. Alive! Permanent. Beautiful. Part of the big show, no longer an outsider.

The more I thought about it, the better it seemed. It made sense. And the more sense it made, the more designs I pictured. There were so many they overflowed. Before long, I was doing illustrations of things I'd never thought about before. I sent some of them along with an article to the editors of *Progressive Architecture* magazine,* and they were kind enough to publish them (February '65). As a result, a tiny new branch of architecture and engineering was born, and

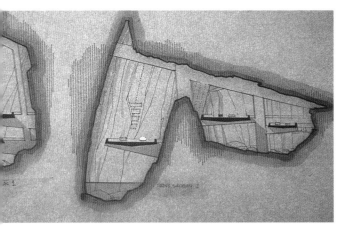

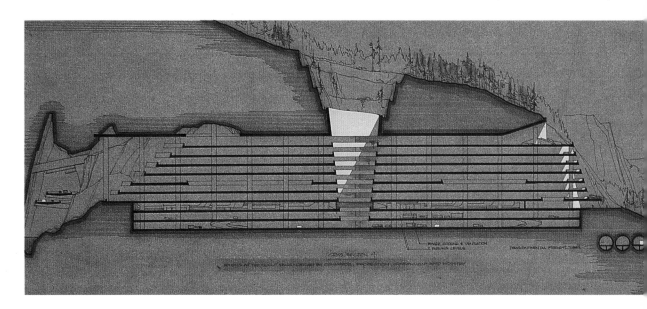

* now merely P/A

now, almost 30 years later, I can report that that tiny branch is … still tiny. Miniscule. But a small band of architects and engineers around the world has been at work getting the bugs out of this new/old way of building. Now it's time to go public. Events seem to be in the saddle, demanding that we pay attention, pushing this gentler kind of construction onto the world stage whether we are ready or not.

"This is all very nice," I can hear you thinking, "this thought of restoring an entire continent to life, but giant dollar signs keep getting in the way."

Mega dollar signs. And we're not even talking about all the other causes demanding the nation's attention. If this gentler kind of infrastructure is ever to take hold among the great works of the 21st century, it's got to capture us whole, body and soul, heads and hearts, as well as guts. It is not a fad, not a temporary measure. It's as elemental as photosynthesis and sunlight.

So. How do we know it will work? Have any scientific studies been done?

The hell with scientific studies. Do you need a scientific study to see that rainwater is repelled by asphalt? … that roofs are dead? … that sunlight and ice and rain make structures rust and crumble and fail prematurely? Do you need a scientist to tell you why weeds push up through abandoned parking lots, turning them into healthy land again if we stay out of the way? No. All you need are eyes.

Malcolm Wells

Look out the window. See, Dick, see? See the buildings, cars, trees, people, roads? Everything looks normal out there, almost benign. There are some ugly places, to be sure, but where's all the killing?

Look again, this time with your eyes closed. Look back a billion years, back a million, back a thousand, then a few hundred. Millenium after millenium, the view is almost unchanging: clean air, transparent waters, wildflowers galore, and a vast land bursting with life and health, even though in the latter millenia Indians are living here.

Now, instead of imagining buildings and roads moving in to kill the land, make believe terrible things start falling out of the sky, doing what we've done with hammers, bulldozers, pipes, and wires. Here they come: blimps, helicopters, jets, hang gliders, balloons, rockets, and space stations, all coming over the ridge – first by the hundreds, then the thousands, then by the millions. They lose altitude and crash into the trees, onto the plains, onto the beaches. Down they come, crushing entire forests, killing vast prairies, torching wetlands and wildlife. Out of the broken skycraft spill lakefuls of fuel and sewage, pesticides and asphalt. Explosions and fires burn everywhere, the air foul, the water toxic. The land is smothered. Native people and wildlife not killed by the invasion try to flee but get pushed into ever smaller areas until the continent is at last defeated.

Just like USA today, in other words, thanks in large part to people like me and all my brother and sister constructors.

Who needs studies or computer models, printouts or water samples to see if we should be building on the earth's tender skin? By hogging all the sunlight wherever we go, we've stamped out much of what we came here for.

Weather is not kind to building materials. They need to be protected by a blanket of earth. Rain drenches our great shipping piers, ice cracks our freeways, water rusts bridge structures, floods rage from impervious neighborhoods.

The new freeway slicing the Johnson farm isn't being built that way primarily to save money. The airport extension filling the bay isn't the result of economic pressures. We just don't know any better. Everything is built the way it's built because life on earth has so far never been the number-one issue in the minds of us who build. All of which brings us squarely up to a line. No one who crosses it can ever cross back again.

In the Nixon years, Bob Haldeman – or was it John Erlichman? – said that once the toothpaste is out of the tube, it's hard to get it back in again.

Well. Whether you like it or not, the toothpaste is now out. The words and drawings in this book can be panned, dismissed, and forgotten, but the idea of a life-supporting infrastructure is with us now. It will be with us as long as we need plants and plants need sunshine.

12.

Now, what do all bridges have in common?

Bridges carry us over things not easily crossed on the surface, things like busy highways, rivers, railroads, and valleys. Bridges are species specific, made for the use of only one of the earth's many creatures.

And bridges sometimes fail dramatically.

But the worst thing about a bridge, any bridge, is what it has in common with all manmade structures: it is a land killer, a dead footprint on land or water. To last for centuries, to provide a sheltered roadway, to serve all creatures, and to present a living surface to the sky, a bridge must have a roof and a deep covering of earth.

16.

A Bridge? … underground?

We like to think that pulling for the underdog is part of the American character. It's a lovely idea but it's only a myth. Ask any Indian or any black person if the underdog gets the breaks here. Ask a grizzly bear, for that matter, or an eagle if support for the underdog is a trait it has seen in us. Ask a river, a forest, or a farm if it's had fair treatment.

Nowhere, perhaps, is our national character flaw more in evidence, visually, than in a bridge. Remember the news item of the deer killed while trying to cross a river span? … run down by a truck, to die its lonely death on the lifeless asphalt? No one reading the story could fail to have been moved. But the selfishness of the bridge-built-to-serve-only-one-of-a-million-species aspect of the news was never aired, never even *considered*.

Well, now it's been aired.

Now it's been aired and dismissed as the woolly-headed thinking of a tree-hugger.

Now it's been aired and dismissed and reconsidered. The fair-play argument begins to take hold in the conscience.

18.

Philadelphia, right now.

Ohio River, 2019 A.D.

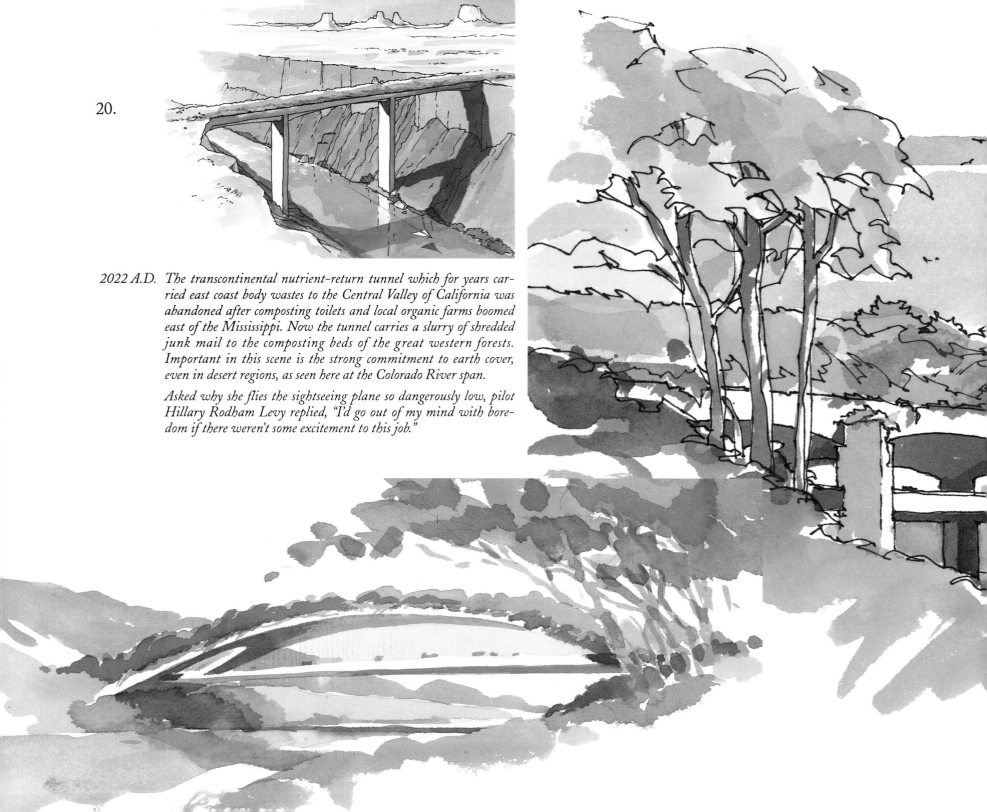

20.

2022 A.D.   *The transcontinental nutrient-return tunnel which for years carried east coast body wastes to the Central Valley of California was abandoned after composting toilets and local organic farms boomed east of the Mississippi. Now the tunnel carries a slurry of shredded junk mail to the composting beds of the great western forests. Important in this scene is the strong commitment to earth cover, even in desert regions, as seen here at the Colorado River span.*

Asked why she flies the sightseeing plane so dangerously low, pilot Hillary Rodham Levy replied, "I'd go out of my mind with boredom if there weren't some excitement to this job."

Is it any better where you live? Is Paris enlightened? Does Rio respect its land? What about Adelaide and Beijing? Or do they too smear asphalt indiscriminately across fields and forests, prairies and wetlands?

No one ever said, "We will now kill all other living creatures by creating dead cities and paved surfaces." It just happened. We took one small step, then, seeing little damage, took another. And that's exactly the way we will *undo* it all: step by step, until the American land is repaved with trees and grasses, eagles and wildflowers.

This is not a transportation discussion; the subject is life on earth. It must be faced, and the sooner we get to it the better.

It's hard to imagine part of Newark, New Jersey, or the industrial section of Los Angeles looking clean and alive like this but it will happen. It must. Once we find our way again as a nation there'll be a new project every month to delight and employ us.

A skeptic, on seeing these huge earth loads supported on such slender legs, said, "one good earth tremor and the whole thing would collapse." She was thinking in terms of today's civil engineering.

The shock-absorbing action of its rubbery stiffness will tend to make this sky tunnel immune to seismic damage. Its space-age surface will make it equally immune to the ravages of weather and sunlight.

The car, or at least some form of private transportation, is here to stay, so we'd better make the best of it with roads that are permanent, safe, benign, and beautiful, not to mention earthlike and appropriate.

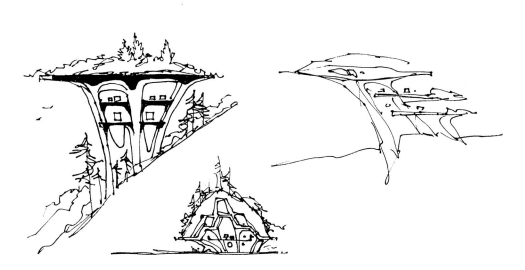

2003 A.D.

Originally called the Transcontinental Expressway, or TCE, this first-built of our extremely high-speed roads soon became known simply as "the slot." Moving at what in the 1990s were racing-car speeds, vehicles could now travel in automated safety from coast to coast in under 10 hours as both drivers and passengers read, dined, and slept. Up above, the undisturbed landscape, its construction wounds healed, could go about its daily business under the sun.

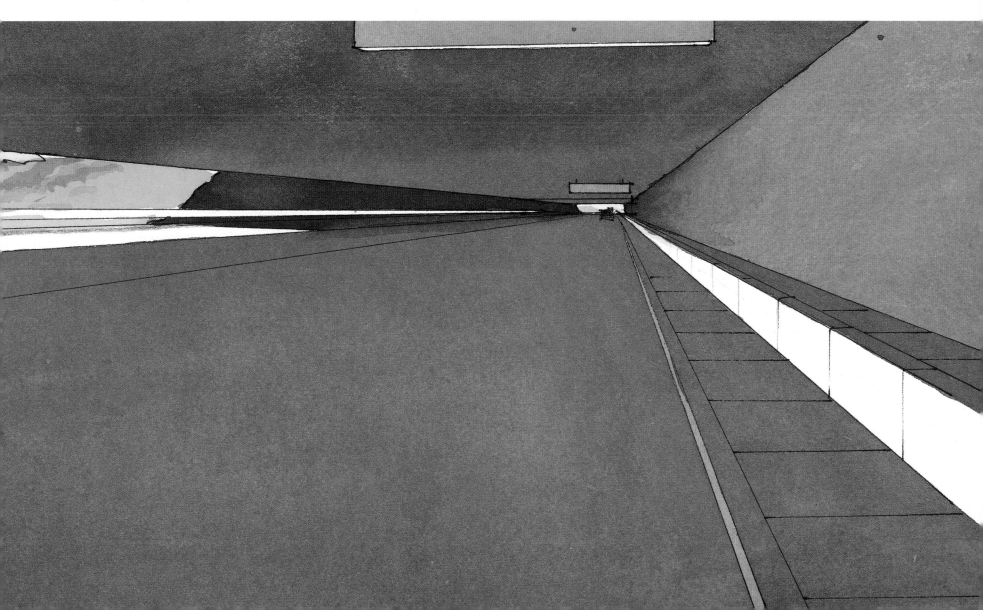

38.

It would be hard to pick from among all the threats to the living world the champion, the king, of the apocalyptic forces. Runaway human population is certainly a candidate, as are those two nuclear horsemen, the bomb and the power plant. But the list holds another tragedy that strikes directly at the richest of the world's breeding grounds: the loss of wetlands.

Shallow water, rich nutrients, and sunlight: there is no habitat friendlier to life. From water plants and insects, fishes and waterfowl, to some of the world's largest mammals, all owe their existence to wet, or periodically wet, terrain.

Beaches can take intensive use without damage as long as the dunes are undisturbed.

Paine's Creek
A watercolor by
Karen North Wells

This semi-rural tidal creek on
Cape Cod is a favorite subject
for painters. It is a metaphor
for all that has been lost by our
destruction of other water-
ways, and it can be a model
— a goal — for their restoration.

What optimism!

What Futility!

A world-famous architect did a prize-winning building ... and treated its waterfront with contempt. Good design should be judged by what it does, not just how it looks.

Regardless of all that, world-famous architects as well as hack designers seem to treat water as if it were an enemy. Why? Do they hate wetlands? Do they see nothing miraculous about what happens where land and water meet? Apparently not. In any case, they see the human use as more important. We have for so long used water as both a dump and a real estate feature it seldom occurs to us that it has higher uses.

"I cover the water-front," was a popular tune in the Big Band era but those words are just as true of us today.

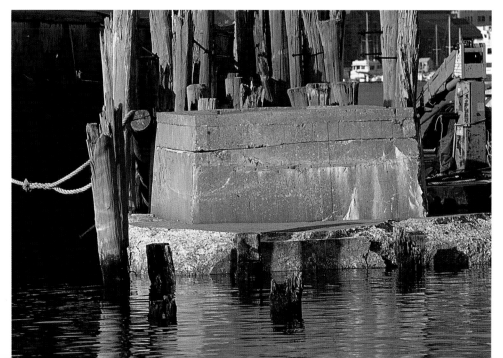

It all depends on how it's covered.

44.

You might think there was no way to use water without destroying its edges. It's hard to imagine a pier and a natural area occupying the same space. But think how a simple boat dock might be built to avoid paving either land or water.

The same kind of thinking applies with equal force to seaports and to the riverfronts of cities. There's no need to destroy the water's edge with port facilities. "Returned to Life" can be the theme if the water's edge is restored. Build the piers in deep water. Let both uses thrive.

This seaport of 2019 A.D. has a great earth-covered roof protecting the entire dock area, presenting to the sun and rain a massive wildgarden that creates, in effect, a green footprint where, before, great lifeless sheets of asphalt and roofing materials had been at work.

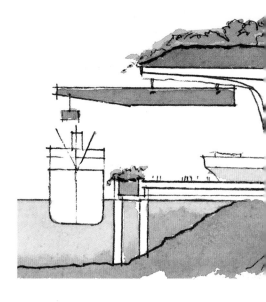

Reaching across from the land to the pier an earth-covered causeway built to last for centuries allows the water's edge to mature to a state of pristine loveliness, alive once again.

Well-tended farms cover a sprawling industrial area just to the the landward of the causeway out to the new seaport.

48.

Few water trips are more beautiful than the ferry rides off the coast of Vancouver where a couple of dollars buy hours of seagoing pleasure among the fir-covered islands. The only sad note is the vast parking lot and vehicle waiting area at the ferry terminal where some **46 lanes** of asphalt pave the sparkling sea. Paving the sea is just as destructive as paving land. Pushed aside by this lifeless waterproofing the living sea takes yet another beating.

Now picture a great earthen roof above that land-linked island of paving. Picture massive earth cover with thousands of tiny fir seedlings planted there. Picture ground covers and fish hawks. Think about the nutrients that would enrich the surrounding sea in the run-off from each rain. The solar engine would be back in business high above the trucks and buses, the cars and foot-passengers, and the land would once again be at peace.

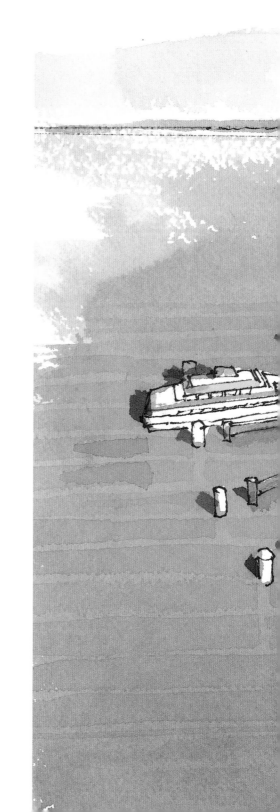

"The wrong side of the tracks" isn't adjacent to the railroad. It's beneath it. A cemetery of crushed earth lies below the rails. Poisoned by human wastes, fuel and cargo leaks, and weed killers, it is a trail of horrors criss-crossing the land.

Trains may be efficient – ton for ton, they beat cars and airplanes by a mile – but the rights of way for the nation's rolling stock lace the land with lines of lifelessness.

Regardless of whether magnetic levitation or some other invention will move the next generation of trains their routes will continue to be land-killers unless we put them in the one place where the right of way is really right, and then require management of all railroad wastes.

2103 A.D.

Outside and inside views of the station at its 100th anniversary, the land undisturbed. Certain stretches of "track," as the lev-ways are still called, occur out of doors to enrich the travelers' experiences.

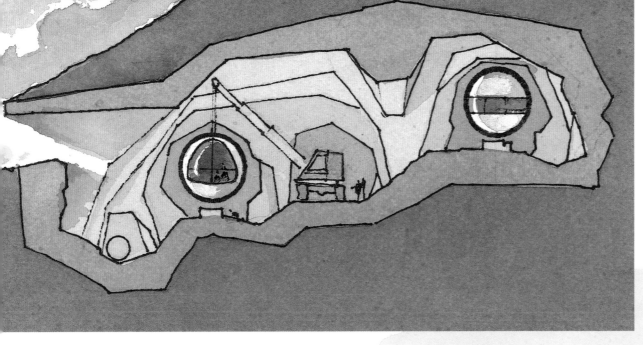

53.

Most of the track is hidden from the weather, from rust and disintegration. Crossing over a riverside highway, however, the trains again appear out of doors for a way.

54.

At the 1998 National Parking Lot Convention (NPLC) the huge sheets of asphalt and concrete in attendance fell into heated argument over which of them was the most wasteful and destructive. The shopping center parking lots were soon left by the wayside for being too intensively used to be considered totally wasteful. Church parking lots then held the lead for a while, claiming that their destruction of thousands of acres of American land combined with their few hours a day of use were unbeatable. They hadn't realized that the parking lots of major sports centers would be even more appalling in both respects. Some of the stadium lots boasted of smothering vast areas of land while being used as seldom as once a month!

The controversy became so heated in '98 that the EPA leaped into the fray, producing within only 6 years the Automobile Storage Act of 2004, which generated buildings like the new Dallas Sports Center, seen at right here with its parking levels lighted for the annual Summer Games.

56.

Is that a tree I see, out there among the bricks and stones, *an actual living tree*? What a life we've created for ourselves!

Living in that deadly dead environment, the tree is a symbol of the way we treat not only each other but the earth beneath our feet as well.

If the world was made to be green and beautiful, and we are its most intelligent creatures, why do we make it so ugly and gray?

Words like "earth cover" and – dare I say it? – "underground" will someday suggest other words like "dry" and "safe" and "sunny" but memories of caves and cellars are still too strong for such associations.

58.

One of the worst things we do – every one of us – is to drop our body wastes into pure, sweet drinking water. Talk about unnatural acts! Ugh. Disgusting. And yet every woman, man, and child performs this act several times a day, apparently unaware that waterless composting toilets create no pollution and work, naturally, in odorless silence.

Will the composting toilet be the toilet of the future? Who can say? Anything will be better than the huge municipal systems now being built all over America in a vain effort to slow the pollution of our waterways.

Home treatment or small-scale treatment of sewage will avoid the massive accidents that always occur when the large systems fail, killing the waters and their creatures with poisons and pollutants.

*Wastes into the river,
wastes into the sky.*

60.

Shown on page 61 is a "Living Machine," as John Todd calls it, large enough to serve a community of between 50,000 and 100,000 people.

"Ecological engineering," he adds, "permits the design of 'Living Machines' – the new eco-technologies for purifying and recycling liquid wastes.

"A Living Machine uses no chemicals and produces only small volumes of sludge, which can be safely composted. A Living Machine waste treatment facility borrows its design principles from ecosystems, including forests and lakes, and includes within it all the major groups of creatures from bacteria to higher plants and animals, including molluscs and fish."

A Living Machine silently at work in Providence, Rhode Island.

62.

Ripping raw materials out of the earth is a brutal act, no matter what the end use is, but if we learn to build 500- and 1000-year structures, changing only their interiors instead of constantly reshaping the land, the brutality, spread out over the ages, may be excusable.

The building below, built in 2004 as a regional shopping center, was later a county office complex (with underground parking, of course) and is now a hospital. Its mantle of earth has not been disturbed in all the 90 years since the original groundbreaking.

LAND SAKES ALIVE!

Before the book is closed on *Infra Structures*, I'd like to say a few final words.

It's unlikely that any of these designs will see the light of day without a lot of refinement. Some of them may prove to be too expensive for even the most dedicated society. All the structures would have to be modified to meet the conditions at their sites. And a few would perhaps just plain not work.

None of this discourages me in the least. This book was written in order to get the *Infra Structures* ideas aired, discussed, criticized, and even shot down. It was written to make us think about stepping more gently upon the land when we build and to help this billion-year journey of ours take a turn for the better after its brief turn for the worse in which 150 years of explosive technology-growth made us build like utter fools.

Malcolm Wells
Underground on Cape Cod
1994

INDEX